QUILTS

AN ENGAGEMENT CALENDAR

1994

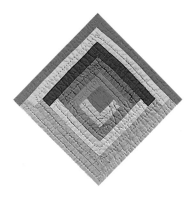

by Susan Jenkins

with Annlee Landman

Illustrations by Anny Evason

A Sterling/Museum Quilts Book
Sterling Publishing Co., Inc. New York

Opposite: MARINER'S COMPASS
c.1890 New York State 67" x 85"

A circle with radiating points is a familiar design, historically associated with many cultures.
The earliest known example of its use as a quilt pattern is in an English quilt inscribed 1726.
This eyecatching example is beautifully pieced and interestingly boasts a center windmill motif
between the 'compasses' and a delightful triple border

Front Cover: LOG CABIN
c.1930 Lancaster County, Pennsylvania 74" x 84"

The Log Cabin quilt became popular in both Europe and America
as early as 1870. This variation is called Light and Dark and is particularly pleasing
with its use of a series of pastel and primary solid color cottons.
This quilt is also featured on the cover of '*Quilts: The American Story*'
by Susan Jenkins, published by Harper Collins, London

Published by Sterling Publishing Company, Inc.
387 Park Avenue South, New York, NY 10016
And by Museum Quilts Publications
254-258 Goswell Road, London EC1V 7EB
Distributed in Canada by Sterling Publishing
c/o Canadian Manda Group, P.O. Box 920, Station U
Toronto, Ontario, Canada M8Z 5P9
Distributed in Australia by Capricorn Link Ltd.
P.O. Box 665 Lane Cove, NSW 2066

Unless otherwise noted, all the quilts featured in this book are from the Susan Jenkins Collection

Illustrations © Anny Evason
Design by Bet Ayer
and Judy Gordon

Printed and bound in Korea

ISBN: 1 897954 00 X

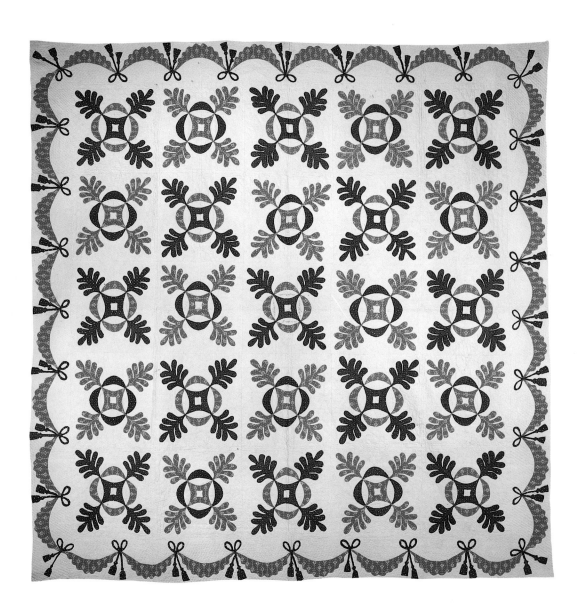

DECEMBER/
JANUARY

27 MONDAY	
28 TUESDAY	○
29 WEDNESDAY	
30 THURSDAY	
31 FRIDAY	
1 SATURDAY New Year's Day	
2 SUNDAY	

OAKLEAF AND REEL
PRESENTATION QUILT
Pennsylvania, USA c.1850
101" x 101"

This handsome quilt is an
individual interpretation of the
traditional Oakleaf and Reel
pattern. It carries a personal
inscription, beautifully written
in indelible ink on the central
block – 'A Donation to the Rev
John Farquhar from the Ladies
of the Chanceford Congregation'.

From the Susan Jenkins Collection

3 MONDAY Holiday (UK)	# JANUARY

4 TUESDAY	
5 WEDNESDAY ◑	
6 THURSDAY	
7 FRIDAY	**TUMBLING BLOCKS** England c.1860 93" x 77"
8 SATURDAY	This High Victorian piece is executed in rich silks, satins and velvet. The dazzling arrangement of a single diamond shape creates a dynamic optical illusion. The use of a three inch velvet tartan ribbon for a binding creates a stylish finish.
9 SUNDAY	*Courtesy Judy Wentworth and Sarah Franklyn, The Antique Textile Company, London, England*

JANUARY

HAWAIIAN APPLIQUE
Hawaii c.1930
80" x 97"

Introduced to quilting in the
19th century by visiting
missionaries, the Hawaiians
rapidly developed their own
distinctive appliqué style
derived from folded cut-paper
designs. The bold and abstract
style of one, usually dark,
color cut from a single piece of
fabric set against white, draws
inspiration from Hawaii's
exotic flora.

*Courtesy John R Sauls, Tyler,
Texas, USA*

10 MONDAY

11 TUESDAY ●

12 WEDNESDAY

13 THURSDAY

14 FRIDAY

15 SATURDAY

16 SUNDAY

JANUARY

17	MONDAY Martin Luther King Jr. Day (USA)
18	TUESDAY
19	WEDNESDAY ◑
20	THURSDAY
21	FRIDAY
22	SATURDAY
23	SUNDAY

**LOG CABIN, LIGHT AND
DARK VARIATION**
USA c.1880
70" x 82"

This pattern dates back to
the 1860's when a new
technique was developed called
Foundation Patchwork. Instead
of seaming the fabric strips
together, quiltmakers 'built' the
Log Cabin block on a square
foundation block beginning at
the centre and working out.

*From the Susan Jenkins
Collection*

JANUARY

MEDALLION SAMPLER
An antique quilt top, recently
quilted by Elreda Johnson.
Pennsylvania, USA c.1850
84" x 84"

This sampler, probably made as
a friendship quilt, features an
unusual collection of medallion
motifs, stitched in vivid
combinations of tiny calico
triangles. The intricately pieced
centre medallion is finely
quilted with hands and hearts.

Courtesy Aly Goodwin,
The N E Horton Antique Quilt
Collection, Black Mountain,
North Carolina, USA

24 MONDAY

25 TUESDAY

26 WEDNESDAY
Australia Day

27 THURSDAY   ○

28 FRIDAY

29 SATURDAY

30 SUNDAY

31 MONDAY

1 TUESDAY

2 WEDNESDAY

3 THURSDAY

4 FRIDAY

5 SATURDAY

6 SUNDAY

JANUARY/
FEBRUARY

MILITARY PATCHWORK
England, c.1870
72" x 76"

The predominance of scarlet
indicates that this quilt was
probably made after 1872,
when scarlet would have
been plentiful in regimental
uniforms, and before 1881,
when the supply of multicolor
pieces used for facings would
have dried up. Thousands of
half inch woollen squares inside
a zigzag border have been sewn
together to make up this
extraordinary patchwork
mosaic.

*Special thanks for information
provided by Mrs S K Hopkins,
Head of the Department of
Uniform, Badges and Medals,
National Army Museum,
Chelsea, London, England.
From the Susan Jenkins
Collection*

FEBRUARY

**PRINCESS FEATHER
APPLIQUE**
Vermont, USA c.1850
80" x 80"

The emblem of the Prince of
Wales, the three feather
plumes, is thought to be the
source of this quilt pattern.
Women presented to court
wore plumes in their hair as a
mark of respect and, of course,
as a statement of fashion. This
example, in stylish turkey red
and green, has extraordinarily
fine quilting of fruit filled
baskets and tiny clam shells.

*From the Susan Jenkins
Collection*

7 MONDAY	
8 TUESDAY	
9 WEDNESDAY	
10 THURSDAY	●
11 FRIDAY	
12 SATURDAY Lincoln's Birthday	
13 SUNDAY	

14	**MONDAY** St Valentine's Day
15	**TUESDAY**
16	**WEDNESDAY** Ash Wednesday
17	**THURSDAY**
18	**FRIDAY** ◑
19	**SATURDAY**
20	**SUNDAY**

FEBRUARY

CUPID'S HEART
Made by Linda M Roy,
Conway, Arkansas, USA 1992
81" x 81"

In the tradition of commemorative quilts but using contemporary fabrics, Linda made this extraordinary appliqué quilt to celebrate her 20th wedding anniversary. The romantic theme has been enhanced by her choice of quilting patterns – cupids, hearts, flowers, wreaths and feathers.

Courtesy International Quilt Festival, Houston, Texas, USA; photo Gary Bankhead

FEBRUARY

**LOG CABIN, STRAIGHT
FURROWS VARIATION**
Berks County, Pennsylvania,
USA c.1880
70" x 71"

The use of subtle shades of
brown with blue accents make
this Mennonite quilt a striking
visual masterpiece. By careful
placement of color, shifting
from dark to light, the viewer's
eye is drawn up along the
diagonal furrows. This quilt is
made from fine dress wools –
fabrics favored by young Amish
and Mennonite women.

*From the Susan Jenkins
Collection*

21	MONDAY Presidents' Day
22	TUESDAY Washington's Birthday
23	WEDNESDAY
24	THURSDAY
25	FRIDAY
26	SATURDAY ○
27	SUNDAY

28 MONDAY	

1 TUESDAY
St David's Day (Wales)

2 WEDNESDAY

3 THURSDAY

4 FRIDAY ◑

5 SATURDAY

6 SUNDAY

FEBRUARY/ MARCH

FEATHERED STAR IN
BLUE AND GOLD
Kentucky, USA c.1920
76" x 78"

A variation of the basic eight
point star design, the feathered
star motif is one of the complex
patchwork designs developed in
the mid 19th century. Its very
complexity assigned it 'showpiece' status, as a quilt brought
out for special occasions.
This example in Wedgewood
blue has been finished with a
delicate sawtooth border
imitating the 'feathering' of the
internal blocks.

*From the Susan Jenkins
Collection*

MARCH

**UNEXPECTED
PLEASURES**
Made by Katrin Pisareva,
St Petersburg, Russia 1991
82" x 56"

Second in the theme category
'This Green & Pleasant Land' at
the 1991 National Patchwork
Championships, UK, this vivid
mosaic patchwork fashioned
from coat cloth celebrates the
artist's opportunity to show her
work outside Russia. She trans-
lates 'this green and pleasant
land' to a more familiar location
– her home town of St
Petersburg – and symbolically
the bird that comes from the
west brings with it the flowers
of hope.

*Courtesy The National
Patchwork Association, Norfolk,
England*

7 MONDAY	
8 TUESDAY	
9 WEDNESDAY	
10 THURSDAY	
11 FRIDAY	
12 SATURDAY	●
13 SUNDAY Mothering Sunday (UK)	

14 MONDAY	

MARCH

15 TUESDAY	

16 WEDNESDAY	

17 THURSDAY St Patrick's Day	

18 FRIDAY	

EMILY'S QUILT
Made by Linda Seward,
London, England 1992
80" x 80"

Linda started this original
design the day she discovered
she was expecting her second
child, and finished it in a timely
fashion the day before Emily
arrived. The pattern provided
an opportunity to practise new
rotary cutting techniques and
to design a complex pattern
using only three fabrics. Linda
machine quilted the pieced
section of the quilt and hand
quilted the wavy water design
in the border.

*Courtesy Linda Seward,
London, England*

19 SATURDAY	

20 SUNDAY First Day of Spring (N. Hemisphere)	◗

MARCH

21	MONDAY
22	TUESDAY
23	WEDNESDAY
24	THURSDAY
25	FRIDAY
26	SATURDAY
27	SUNDAY ○ Palm Sunday · Passover · British Summer Time begins

WELSH STRIPPY IN RED
AND BLUE
Dyfed, Wales c.1890
78" x 84"

This thoroughly Welsh quilt
is a masterpiece of quilting
technique – dramatic in its
color design, simple in its
piecing and exquisitely stitched
with a catalogue of challenging
quilting patterns. The simple
and strong design qualities of
Welsh quilts bear an outstanding resemblance to Amish
quilts.

*Courtesy Ron Simpson, London,
England*

28 MONDAY

29 TUESDAY

30 WEDNESDAY

31 THURSDAY

1 FRIDAY
Good Friday · April Fool's Day

2 SATURDAY

3 SUNDAY
Easter Sunday ◑

MARCH/ APRIL

DOVE AT THE WINDOW
Western Pennsylvania, USA
c.1880
80" x 94"

An amazing quilt which
features both rich colors and
startling design. A combination
of nine-Patch posts, pieced bar
sashing and Flying Geese border
surround the intricate internal
blocks to create a rich mosaic
with an intriguing three-
dimensional effect.

*From the Susan Jenkins
Collection*

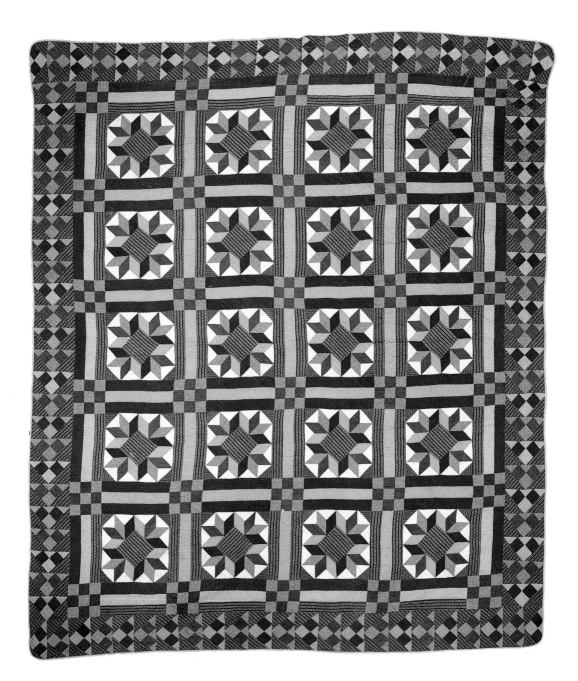

APRIL

AMISH LONE STAR
Texas, USA c.1920
82" x 88"

Variously known as Star of
Bethlehem and Star of the East,
star quilts of this sort were
generally only brought out for
Christmas. This mesmerising
example is pieced point by
point. Forty-eight diamonds of
equal size are arranged in rows
of different lengths to form the
eight diamond shaped points.
The star is asymmetrically
placed, allowing for an exceptionally beautiful detailed
pillow panel. The coverlet is
finished with the distinctive
triangle and scallop edge border
popular between 1925-50.

*From the Susan Jenkins
Collection*

4	MONDAY
Easter Monday (UK Holiday, except Scotland)
5	TUESDAY
6	WEDNESDAY
7	THURSDAY
8	FRIDAY
9	SATURDAY
10	SUNDAY

11 MONDAY ●

12 TUESDAY

13 WEDNESDAY

14 THURSDAY

15 FRIDAY

16 SATURDAY

17 SUNDAY

APRIL

SCOTTIES
Indiana, USA c.1930
79" x 91"

Contemporary events inspired commercial pattern houses to create a catalogue of new and often light hearted quilt patterns. The Roosevelt presidency was commemorated with a Roosevelt Rose, eagle designs symbolised the National Recovery Act and the Scottie dog became a celebrated quilt motif after Roosevelt's speech about his little dog Fala.

Courtesy John R Sauls, Tyler, Texas, USA

APRIL

TO ENGLAND WITH LOVE
Made by Zena Thorpe,
Chatsworth, California, USA
1990
72" x 72"

Winner of the 1990 UK
National Patchwork Champion-
ship, this contemporary quilt is
a collage of the artist's loving
memories of her youth in
England. 'There'll always be an
England' appears in the lace
doily surrounding the central
panel. The reverse side of the
quilt depicts the British
symbols of the bulldog and the
Union Jack.

*Courtesy the National
Patchwork Association, Norfolk,
England*

18 MONDAY

19 TUESDAY   ◑

20 WEDNESDAY

21 THURSDAY

22 FRIDAY

23 SATURDAY
St George's Day (England)

24 SUNDAY

25 MONDAY		○

26 TUESDAY	

27 WEDNESDAY	

28 THURSDAY	

29 FRIDAY	

30 SATURDAY	

1 SUNDAY	

LOVE APPLE
Pennsylvania, USA c.1870
84" x 76"

Also known as Pomegranate,
the mythical fruit of love and
abundance, this charming
appliqué quilt boasts a stylish
chrome yellow, pink and
green motif which is gaily set
on an intricately quilted ground
and surrounded by a handsome
diamond border.

*From the Susan Jenkins
Collection*

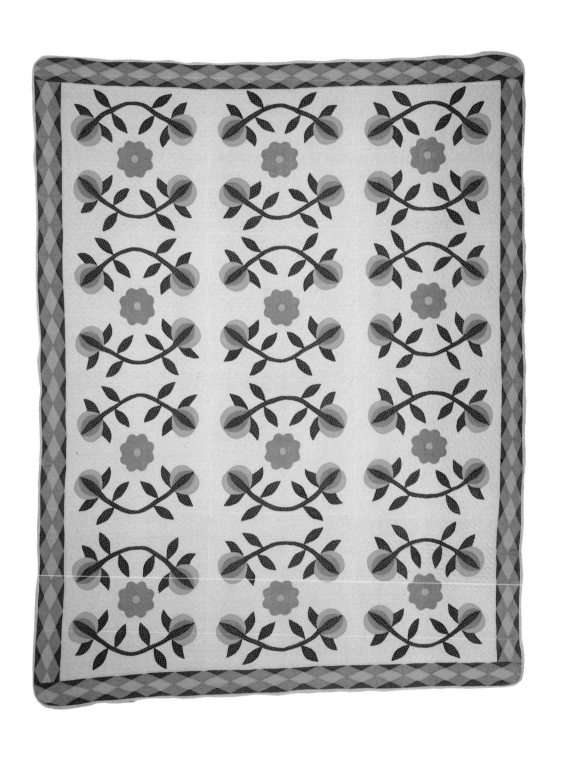

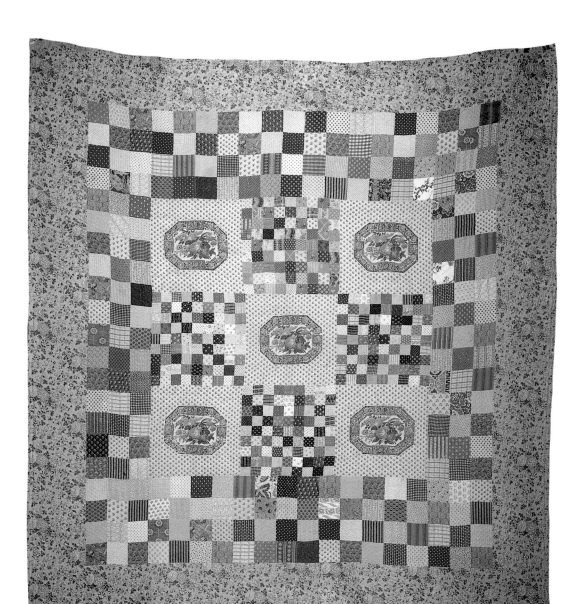

MAY

**PRINCESS CHARLOTTE
COMMEMORATIVE
PATCHWORK**
England c.1816
103" x 96"

Five flower-filled medallions
printed to celebrate the
Princess's marriage in 1816
have been used as the foundation for this historic quilt. The
medallion border bears the
Royal Coat of Arms, the
Princess's feathers, two crowns
and a legend which reads:
'Princess Charlotte of Wales
married to Leopold Prince of
Saxe-Coburg, May 2 1816'.

*Courtesy Judy Wentworth and
Sarah Franklyn, The Antique
Textile Company, London,
England*

---

2 MONDAY
May Day Holiday (UK, except Scotland)   ◗

3 TUESDAY

4 WEDNESDAY

5 THURSDAY

6 FRIDAY

7 SATURDAY

8 SUNDAY
Mother's Day (USA, Canada, Australia)

9 MONDAY	
10 TUESDAY	●
11 WEDNESDAY	
12 THURSDAY Ascension Day	
13 FRIDAY	
14 SATURDAY	
15 SUNDAY	

MAY

LOG CABIN,
COURT HOUSE STEPS
VARIATION
USA c.1930
78" x 92"

Log Cabin designs date back to the 1840 presidential race when General William Harrison ran a 'log cabin and cider barrel' election campaign. The log cabin represented the virtues attached to simple country living, an idea effectively used later by Abraham Lincoln. This graphic quilt is one of six variations of log cabin quilts, each of which employs a different arrangement of light and dark strips.

From the Susan Jenkins Collection

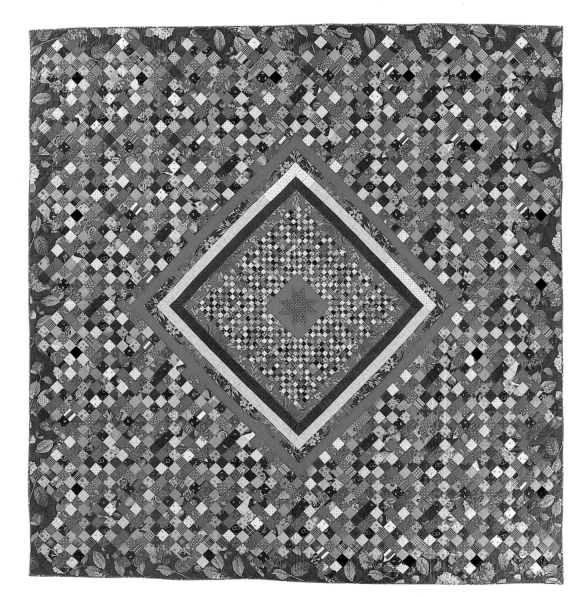

MAY

16 MONDAY

17 TUESDAY

18 WEDNESDAY ◐

19 THURSDAY

20 FRIDAY

21 SATURDAY

22 SUNDAY
Whit Sunday

POSTAGE STAMP
DIAMOND IN SQUARE
Pennsylvania, USA c.1870
79" x 79"

Advances in colorfast dyes and
roller printing created a greater
variety of cheap cotton prints
offering women a wonderful
choice for making scrap quilts.
This awe-inspiring one-patch
pattern quilt is testimony to the
quilter's skill and patience.
Thousands of squares measur-
ing less than one inch each have
been cut and stitched together.

*Courtesy Shelly Zegart,
Kentucky, USA*

23 MONDAY Victoria Day (Canada)	# MAY

23 MONDAY
Victoria Day (Canada)

24 TUESDAY

25 WEDNESDAY   ○

26 THURSDAY

27 FRIDAY

28 SATURDAY

29 SUNDAY
Trinity Sunday

OHIO STAR
USA c.1840
76" x 90"

This stunning quilt, with its
combination of a rare copper-
plate Regency pillar print in the
border and blank blocks and the
array of Provençal inspired
prints in pieced Ohio star
blocks, is a textile enthusiast's
dream. Regency fabrics were
strongly influenced by classical
themes, hence the penchant for
Greek and Roman columns.
The star is one of the oldest
and most popular quilt motifs
and at least 100 variations can
be identified.

*From the Susan Jenkins
Collection*

MAY/JUNE

CELESTIAL GARDEN
Made by Betty Jo Shiell and
Grace Anderson,
Florida, USA 1992
88" x 88"

This lovely quilt received an
honorable mention in the
Traditional Pieced (Large)
category of the American
International Quilt Association
Judged Show at the Inter-
national Quilt Festival,
Houston, Texas. As long-time
friends Grace and Betty
combined their individual
expertise – Grace's piecing and
quilting and Betty Jo's broderie
perse chintz appliqué – to make
this floral fantasy.

*Courtesy The International
Quilt Festival, Houston, Texas,
USA*

30 MONDAY
Memorial Day (USA) · Spring Holiday (UK)

31 TUESDAY

1 WEDNESDAY ◑

2 THURSDAY

3 FRIDAY

4 SATURDAY

5 SUNDAY

6	MONDAY

7	TUESDAY

8	WEDNESDAY

9	THURSDAY	●

10	FRIDAY

11	SATURDAY

12	SUNDAY

JUNE

GOD BLESS OUR HOME
Made by Mary Dora
Kreyenhagen,
Ohio, USA c.1945
84" x 102"

Mary Kreyenhagen, a local
quilter and artist, created this
quilt 'story book' in the manner
of a cross-stitch sampler at the
end of World War II with
fabrics purchased from
Hanson's Dry Goods Store in
Bethesda, Maryland. Mary
stitched herself into this quilt,
next to letters C and P. Making
quilts to tell a story or celebrate
the history of one's family,
home or community has been a
popular pursuit among
American quilters since the
early 19th century.

Courtesy Shelly Zegart,
Kentucky, USA

JUNE

13	MONDAY
14	TUESDAY Flag Day (USA)
15	WEDNESDAY
16	THURSDAY ◑
17	FRIDAY
18	SATURDAY
19	SUNDAY Father's Day

FLORAL APPLIQUE
USA c.1930
88" x 104"

One of the thousands of quilt patterns which were published in the USA in the 1930s, this appealing floral appliqué uses the new pastel shades which were fashionable between the wars. This exuberant example is carefully appliquéd in a series of cheerful bouquets which wind their way around the border.

From the Susan Jenkins Collection

20 MONDAY

21 TUESDAY
Summer begins (N. Hemisphere)

22 WEDNESDAY

23 THURSDAY   ○

24 FRIDAY
St. Jean-Baptiste (Canada)

25 SATURDAY

26 SUNDAY

JUNE

SUNBURST
Maryland, USA c.1900
75" x 73"

Thirty-two diamond shaped pieces of printed fabric radiate from a solid eight point central star to make a large hexagon. This dramatic pattern demands outstanding precision in work-manship, as any inaccuracy multiplies visibly as the star grows.

Courtesy Willem and Barbara Ann D Calsem, New Orleans, Louisiana, USA

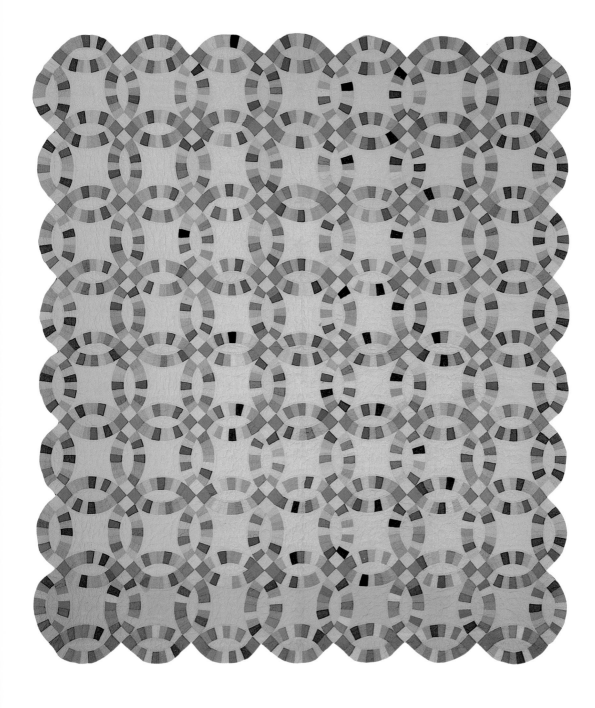

JUNE/JULY

**DOUBLE WEDDING
RING**
USA c.1930
72" x 82"

This challenging pattern of
interlocking rings, thought to be
a German design originally,
came to symbolize the bands of
marriage. It was introduced in
the mid 19th century and
reached its height of popularity
in the early 20th century with
the advent of pre-cut templates,
which made this exacting
pattern very much easier to
make.

*From the Susan Jenkins
Collection*

27 MONDAY

28 TUESDAY

29 WEDNESDAY

30 THURSDAY   ◑

1 FRIDAY
Canada Day (Canada)

2 SATURDAY

3 SUNDAY

JULY

4	MONDAY Independence Day (USA)
5	TUESDAY
6	WEDNESDAY
7	THURSDAY
8	FRIDAY ●
9	SATURDAY
10	SUNDAY

FLAGS
Arkansas, USA 1942
76" x 86"

For generations women have made quilts for fund raising purposes. During the two world wars many American women chose this way of 'doing their bit' for their country and the boys abroad. This quilt, made by the Pleasant View House Demonstration Club and raffled at 10 cents a ticket, was won by Mr Kenny McAlister of the Baker Street Community.

Courtesy Cindy Rennels, Oklahoma, USA

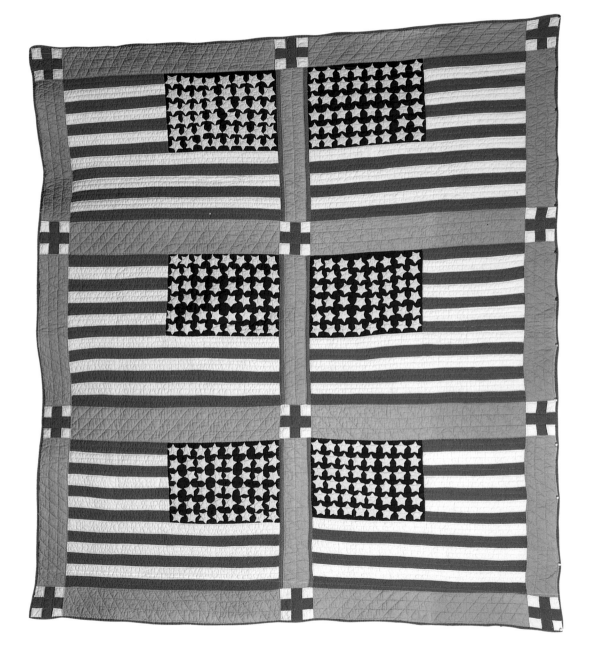

JULY

11 MONDAY

12 TUESDAY

13 WEDNESDAY

14 THURSDAY

15 FRIDAY

16 SATURDAY   ◗

17 SUNDAY

POPPYFIELD II
Made by Pat Derrick,
Norfolk, England
23" x 27"

Dozens of dazzling poppies
seem ready to burst through
the borders of this marvellous
modern day quilt. Indeed, Pat
Derrick took her inspiration
from the Norfolk poppyfields.
The high saturation colors have
been carefully hand dyed from
cotton and pieced over paper.

*Courtesy The Quilters Guild,
Derbyshire, England; photo
Elvin Derrick*

18 MONDAY

19 TUESDAY

20 WEDNESDAY

21 THURSDAY

22 FRIDAY ○

23 SATURDAY

24 SUNDAY

JULY

AMISH TUMBLING BLOCKS
Holmes County, Ohio, USA
c.1940
86" x 77"

Tumbling Blocks or Baby Blocks is a deceptively simple quilt pattern which features an intriguing interplay of color and dimension. The arrangement of light and dark shades creates an exhilarating optical illusion. This pattern achieved great popularity during the Victorian period.

From the Susan Jenkins Collection

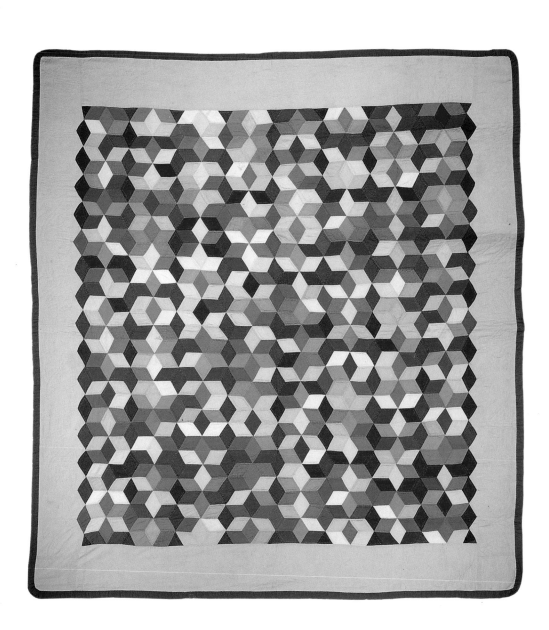

JULY

25 MONDAY

26 TUESDAY

27 WEDNESDAY

28 THURSDAY

29 FRIDAY

30 SATURDAY ◐

31 SUNDAY

BERRIES
Pennsylvania, USA c.1880
74" x 80"

This cornucopia of berries sweeping into a secondary design of circles has been conceived in the favorite palette of 19th century central Pennsylvanian appliqué artists – solid red and green on a white base with chrome yellow high-lights. The berries are carefully appliquéd and stuffed (trapunto work) to create a heightened three dimensional effect.

From the Susan Jenkins Collection

1 MONDAY
Civic Holiday (Canada) · Summer Holiday (Scotland)

2 TUESDAY

3 WEDNESDAY

4 THURSDAY

5 FRIDAY

6 SATURDAY

7 SUNDAY ●

AUGUST

WHEEL OF FORTUNE
USA c.1890
70" x 86"

Rural quilters in America exchanged patterns through household and farm periodicals, and Wheel of Fortune became a firm favorite in the repertoire of available quilt patterns. A variation of the Mariner's Compass, this quilt makes exciting use of indigo and cheddar.

From the Susan Jenkins Collection

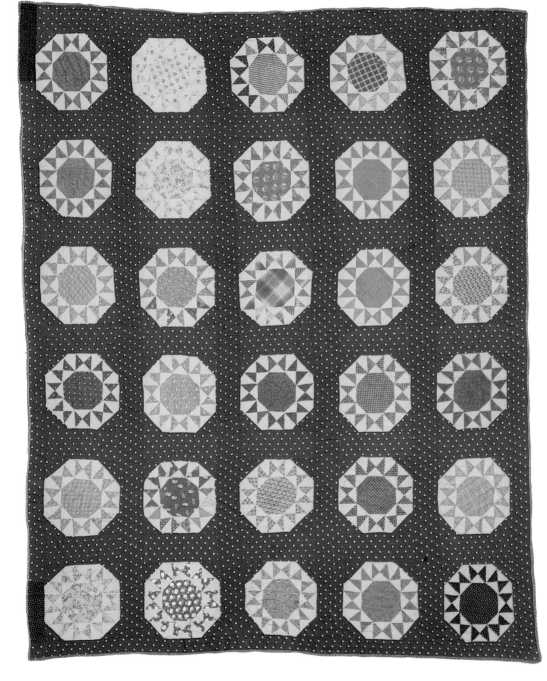

AUGUST

FAN VARIATION
Ohio, USA late 1880s
78" x 70"

This intoxicating and unusual variation of the fan and snow-ball pattern is achieved with five strongly contrasting yet wholly sympathetic colored woollens. The vibrant graphic sophistication of this quilt prefigures the work of much 20th century modern art.

Courtesy Willem and Barbara Ann D Calsem, New Orleans, Louisiana, USA

8 MONDAY

9 TUESDAY

10 WEDNESDAY

11 THURSDAY

12 FRIDAY

13 SATURDAY

14 SUNDAY   ◑

15 MONDAY	

16 TUESDAY	

17 WEDNESDAY	

18 THURSDAY	

19 FRIDAY	

20 SATURDAY	

21 SUNDAY	○

AUGUST

CHINTZ SUNFLOWER
Made by Mollie Parsons Pratt,
Morven, North Carolina, USA
c.1830
86" x 92"

This 'showpiece' quilt in
pristine condition remained
with the maker's family until it
was sold in 1992. The striking
textiles, including a selection of
glazed and unglazed chintzes
and 'blue resist', would have
arrived in America from India
by way of England.

Courtesy Aly Goodwin,
The N E Horton Antique Quilt
Collection, Black Mountain,
North Carolina, USA

AUGUST

22	MONDAY
23	TUESDAY
24	WEDNESDAY
25	THURSDAY
26	FRIDAY
27	SATURDAY
28	SUNDAY

ANTRIM BED
FURNITURE
Ireland 18th century
60" x 62"

This exquisite bed cover
embroidered with gold silk on
satin is part of a set made by or
under the instruction of Lady
Helena McDonnell (1705-
1783), the sister of the 5th Earl
of Antrim. The set, originally
made as a wedding gift,
includes a coverlet, valances
and cushion, pillow and bolster
covers.

*Courtesy The Ulster Museum,
Belfast, Northern Ireland*

29 MONDAY
Summer Holiday (UK except Scotland)

30 TUESDAY

31 WEDNESDAY

1 THURSDAY

2 FRIDAY

3 SATURDAY

4 SUNDAY

AUGUST/ SEPTEMBER

PINEAPPLE LOG CABIN TRAPUNTO
Pennsylvania, USA c.1860
68" x 75"

This unusual Mennonite quilt with its elegant trapunto work is a variation of the Log Cabin pattern. It is made of a combination fabric known as *linsey-woolsey*, in which the warp is linen and the weft is wool. This fabric was particularly popular for household furnishings in the 18th and early 19th centuries.

Courtesy Aly Goodwin, The N E Horton Antique Quilt Collection, Black Mountain, North Carolina, USA, and Rocky Mountain Quilts, Colorado, USA.

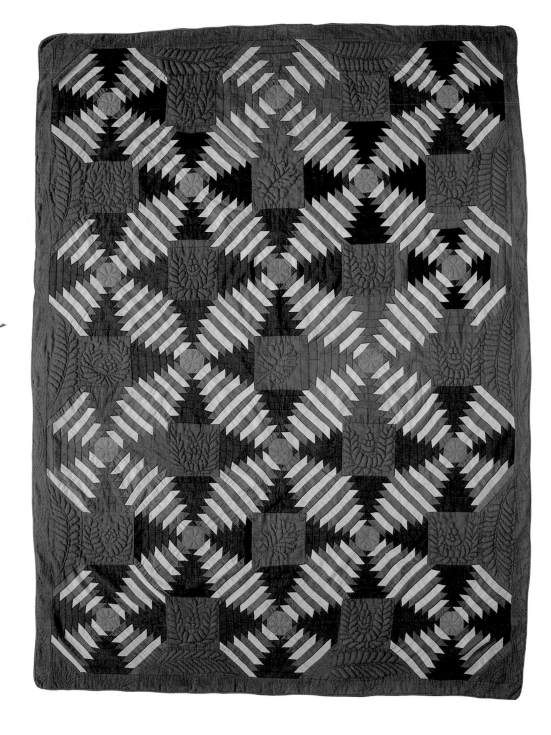

SEPTEMBER

**PRIMITIVE SCHOOL
HOUSES**
Vermont, USA c.1880
60" x 70"

The one-room school house is a popular and symbolic motif in American culture. In the un-settled and dangerous world of the new frontier it represented an achievement of stability and permanence.

From the Susan Jenkins Collection

5 MONDAY
Labor Day (USA, Canada)   ●

6 TUESDAY
Rosh Hashanah

7 WEDNESDAY
Rosh Hashanah

8 THURSDAY

9 FRIDAY

10 SATURDAY

11 SUNDAY

12 MONDAY	◑
13 TUESDAY	
14 WEDNESDAY	
15 THURSDAY Yom Kippur	
16 FRIDAY	
17 SATURDAY	
18 SUNDAY	

SEPTEMBER

GRANDMOTHER'S FLOWER GARDEN
England c.1780
100" x 110"

This exceptionally fine English patchwork of colorful, hexagonal flower motifs cut from dress fabrics is a celebration of 18th century needlework. Like many patchworks of this period, the piece is not quilted.

Courtesy Sarah Franklyn and Judy Wentworth, The Antique Textile Company, London, England

SEPTEMBER

ANNE PRICE
Wales 1835
96" x 86"

Made up of a series of geometrically varied chintz borders around a central block with floral appliqué, this quilt is a variation of the medallion style. Signed and dated in cross-stitch, it uses a multitude of printed dress cottons fashionable during the mid 19th century.

Courtesy Ron Simpson, London, England

---

19 MONDAY ○

20 TUESDAY

21 WEDNESDAY

22 THURSDAY

23 FRIDAY
Autumn begins (N. Hemisphere)

24 SATURDAY

25 SUNDAY

26 MONDAY	
27 TUESDAY	
28 WEDNESDAY ◑	
29 THURSDAY	
30 FRIDAY	
1 SATURDAY	
2 SUNDAY	

SEPTEMBER /OCTOBER

FLANNEL BASKET
Made by Mrs Ann Shanks,
Benwell, Newcastle-upon-Tyne
c.1910
83" x 59"

This quilt is made from brightly
colored utility flannels and
suitings. From the central
basket appliqué we can assume
that it was made around the
time of Mrs Shanks' marriage.

*Courtesy Beamish, The North of
England Open Air Museum,
County Durham, England*

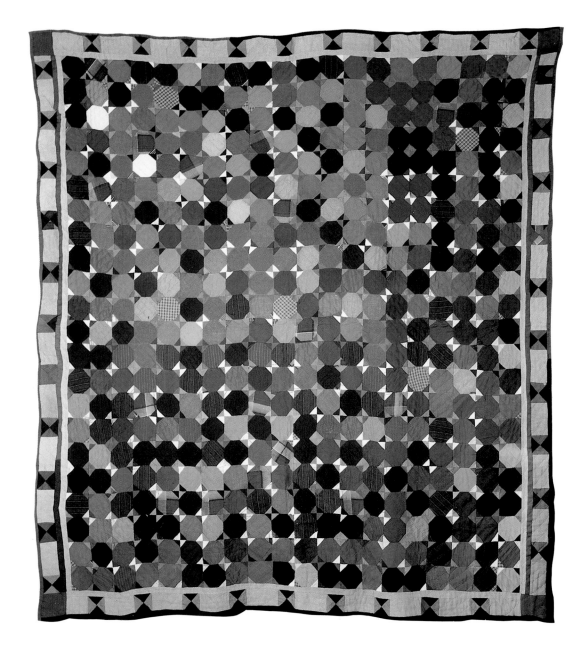

OCTOBER

MENNONITE OCTAGON
USA c.1880
78" x 82"

The small and delicate piece-work within a restrained geometric border provides a striking contrast to the profusion of thick woollen clothing scraps. This robust quilt is marvellously idiosyncratic, with its uneven distribution of colored patches seemingly placed without rhyme or reason.

From the Susan Jenkins Collection

3 MONDAY

4 TUESDAY

5 WEDNESDAY ●

6 THURSDAY

7 FRIDAY

8 SATURDAY

9 SUNDAY

10 MONDAY
Columbus Day (USA) · Thanksgiving Day (Canada)

11 TUESDAY

12 WEDNESDAY

13 THURSDAY

14 FRIDAY

15 SATURDAY

16 SUNDAY

OCTOBER

THE LENNOX QUILT
Made by Martha Lennox,
Ireland 1712
84" x 96"

This is a stunning example of
18th century Irish needlework,
combining a penchant for
things oriental with a delicately
observed English naturalism.
Martha Lennox spent thirty
pounds, a vast amount of
money in the 18th century, on
French embroidery silk to
complete this brilliantly colored
and stitched heirloom piece.

*Courtesy The Ulster Museum,
Belfast, Northern Ireland*

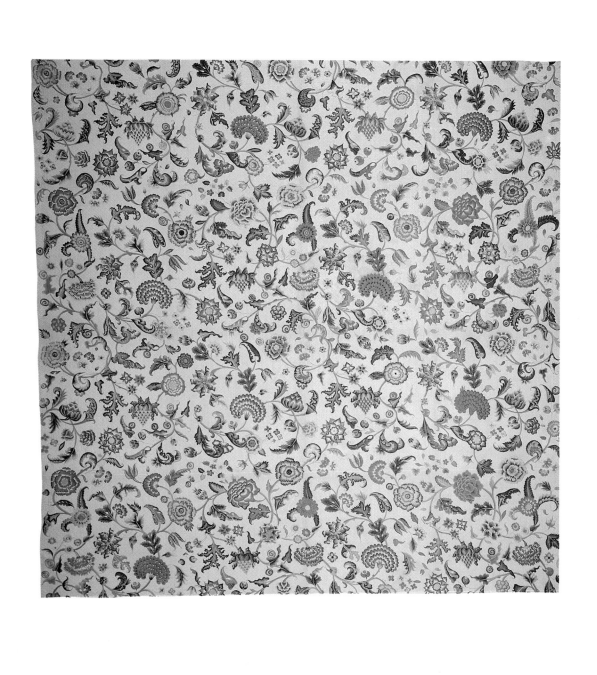

OCTOBER

17 MONDAY	
18 TUESDAY	
19 WEDNESDAY	○
20 THURSDAY	
21 FRIDAY	
22 SATURDAY	
23 SUNDAY British Summer Time ends	

CROWN OF THORNS
Amish, Ohio, USA c.1940
73" x 73"

Although deeply devout, the
Amish quilter used few patterns
with an obvious religious
connection. The Crown of
Thorns is a rare exception to
this rule. This handsome quilt
in lavender on black has border
quilting in fine rope stitching,
while its central blocks feature
a fanciful harp quilting.

*From the Susan Jenkins
Collection*

24 MONDAY	

25 TUESDAY	

26 WEDNESDAY	

27 THURSDAY	◐

28 FRIDAY	

29 SATURDAY	

30 SUNDAY	

OCTOBER

CHERRY BASKETS
USA c.1930
70" x 84"

The basket is a much loved and popular quilt motif. This light hearted quilt, with its jaunty and irregular baskets in colorful cotton prints, is an example of pieced and appliqué work.

From the Susan Jenkins Collection

OCTOBER/
NOVEMBER

FAMOUS FACES
Made by Sophia Serena
Schroeder, Indiana, USA
c.1950
53" x 73"

This novelty quilt-cum-wall-
hanging of dolls' heads has been
pieced onto a linen backing.
The faces are embroidered like-
nesses of household names of
the 1940s and 1950s, including
Bette Davis, Roy Rogers, Joan
Crawford and Imelda Marcos.
In the tradition of Rembrandt,
Velazquez and other great
masters, the artist has included
herself in the picture – in
profile wearing a pink bonnet.

Courtesy Shelly Zegart,
Kentucky, USA

31 MONDAY Halloween	
1 TUESDAY	
2 WEDNESDAY	
3 THURSDAY	●
4 FRIDAY	
5 SATURDAY Guy Fawkes Night (UK)	
6 SUNDAY	

7 MONDAY	

8 TUESDAY Election Day (USA)	

9 WEDNESDAY	

10 THURSDAY	◑

11 FRIDAY Veterans' Day (USA) · Remembrance Day (Canada)	

12 SATURDAY	

13 SUNDAY Remembrance Sunday (UK)	

NOVEMBER

VICTORIAN CRAZY CRIB
QUILT
USA c.1890
18" x 24"

The Crazy Quilt was a curious
invention of the Victorian
period. Rather than geometric
pieces of cotton calico, irregular
shaped scraps of velvet,
brocade and taffeta were used,
often from worn out garments
and furnishing fabrics. This
piece is unusual because it
features a central medallion of
an embroidered bouquet of
daisies and a traditional nine-
patch block. But, in common
with all crazy quilts, it includes
decorative top-stitching with a
catalog of embroidered stitches.

*Courtesy Museum Quilts
Picture Library*

NOVEMBER

SAMPLER QUILT
Made by Mamie Druckenbrod,
Schoneck, Pennsylvania, USA
c.1895
78" x 88"

This charming quilt is a window
on the domestic life of 11 year
old Mamie Druckenbrod, made
one year before her marriage to
William Hainly. At once child-
like and sophisticated, the
various blocks with personal
inscriptions record events or
symbols important to the
maker. Daisy and Polly were
the family dog and parrot, and
the postcard is a discreet
reference to her beloved
brother Adam, who ran away
from home to Illinois.

Courtesy Aly Goodwin,
The N E Horton Antique Quilt
Collection, Black Mountain,
North Carolina, USA, and
Rocky Mountain Quilts,
Colorado, USA

14	MONDAY
15	TUESDAY
16	WEDNESDAY
17	THURSDAY
18	FRIDAY ○
19	SATURDAY
20	SUNDAY

21	MONDAY

22	TUESDAY

23	WEDNESDAY

24	THURSDAY Thanksgiving Day (USA)

25	FRIDAY

26	SATURDAY ◑

27	SUNDAY First Sunday in Advent

NOVEMBER

ALBUM QUILT
Made by Mary E Rutland,
North Carolina, USA c.1860
78" x 84"

This album quilt was made by
Mary E Rutland, an African-
American woman in the
Smithville District of Brunswick
County, North Carolina. Each
of the sixteen blocks feature
familiar objects and symbols,
such as a soup kettle, cotton
balls and crucifixes, which
document the maker's life.
The abundance of heart motifs
quilted on the background
suggests this may have been
made to commemorate a
wedding.

*From the Susan Jenkins
Collection*

NOVEMBER/
DECEMBER

PICTORIAL FELT QUILT
Mohawk, NewYork, USA c.1890
94" x 100"

This striking quilt is a record of a
wealthy family building a house.
They travelled to Europe to buy
furniture and objets d'art for
their new home. These, and their
memories of the great sights on
the Continent, inspired the
pictorial images.

*Courtesy Shelly Zegart, Kentucky,
USA*

28	MONDAY First Day of Hanukkah
29	TUESDAY
30	WEDNESDAY St Andrew's Day (Scotland)
1	THURSDAY
2	FRIDAY ●
3	SATURDAY
4	SUNDAY

5 MONDAY

6 TUESDAY

7 WEDNESDAY

8 THURSDAY

9 FRIDAY ◗

10 SATURDAY

11 SUNDAY

DECEMBER

LONE STAR
Wales c.1885
84" x 78"

This cotton quilt is unusually bright, as Welsh quilters generally favored more sober colors. The elaborate piecing of the star and the diamond border is reminiscent of Islamic tiling, while the back is a strippy design, typical of North Country English and Welsh quilts.

Courtesy Ron Simpson, London, England

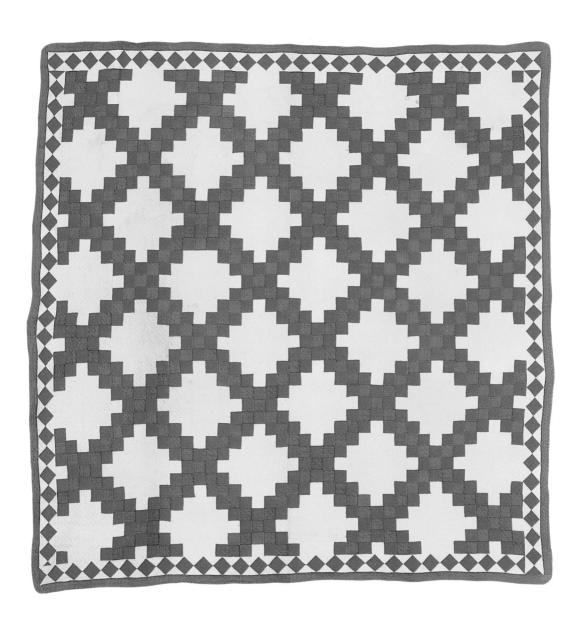

DECEMBER

DOUBLE IRISH CHAIN
Delaware Co., Pennsylvania,
USA c.1880
84" x 90"

The Irish Chain, a relatively
simple pattern dating back to
the 19th century, has long been
popular as a beginner's quilt,
and is sometimes used in scrap
and other utility quilts.
However, this example in
fashionable turkey red, green
and cream, finely quilted
within an elegant pieced
border, must have been made
by a very capable needlewoman
and kept for special guests.

*From the Susan Jenkins
Collection*

12 MONDAY	
13 TUESDAY	
14 WEDNESDAY	
15 THURSDAY	
16 FRIDAY	
17 SATURDAY	
18 SUNDAY	○

DECEMBER

19 MONDAY

20 TUESDAY

21 WEDNESDAY

22 THURSDAY
Winter begins (N. Hemisphere)

23 FRIDAY

24 SATURDAY
Christmas Eve

25 SUNDAY
Christmas Day ◗

MENNONITE JOSEPH'S COAT
Pennsylvania c.1920
70" x 78"

Inspired by the Biblical story about Joseph's coat of many colors, this extravagant quilt is a visual feast. The rainbow colored stripes are simply repeated with each column quilted in a different pattern – diamonds, chains, braids, feathers – to give a rich and varied textural effect.

From the Susan Jenkins Collection

DECEMBER/
JANUARY

EVERGREEN
Texas, USA c.1920
66" x 86"

The tree, in all its varieties, has
been a popular motif in
American quilt making. This
seasonal quilt was made from a
kit during the 1920s when
commercially printed patterns
encouraged quilters to embark
on new and challenging projects.
Commercial patterns meant
that quilts were no longer
exclusively one-of-a-kind, but
they fuelled the grass roots
revival in quilting.

*From the Susan Jenkins
Collection*

26 MONDAY
Boxing Day

27 TUESDAY

28 WEDNESDAY

29 THURSDAY

30 FRIDAY

31 SATURDAY

1 SUNDAY
New Year's Day ●

ACKNOWLEDGEMENTS

Grateful thanks to the following collectors and institutions who generously contributed the use of their quilts for inclusion in this publication:

Beamish, The North of England Open Air Museum, Beamish, Co. Durham DH9 0RG, England

Willem & Barbara Ann D van Calsem, The Front Porch, 824 Royal Street, New Orleans, LA 70116, USA

Aly Goodwin, Black Mountain Antiques Mall, 100 Sutton Avenue, Black Mountain, NC 28711, USA

The National Patchwork Association, PO Box 300, Hethersett, Norwich, Norfolk NR9 3DB, England

Cindy Rennels, Cindy's Quilts, Box 1212, Clinton, OK 73601, USA

Rocky Mountain Quilts, 3847 Alt 6 & 24, Palisade, CO 81526, USA

John R Sauls, 310 West Rusk, Tyler, TX 75701, USA

Ron Simpson, Portobello Road, London W11, England

The Antique Textile Company, 100 Portland Road, London W11 4LQ, England

The International Quilt Festival, 14520 Memorial Drive, Suite 54, Houston, TX 77079, USA

The Quilters Guild, OP66 Dean Clough, Halifax, W Yorkshire HX3 5AX, England

The Ulster Museum, Botanic Gardens, Belfast BT9 5AB, Northern Ireland

Shelly Zegart, 12Z River Hill Road, Louisville, KY 40207, USA

Special thanks to the following contemporary quilters for graciously allowing us to feature their work:
Grace Anderson, Pat Derrick, Elreda Johnson, Katrin Pisareva, Linda M Roy, Linda Seward, Betty Jo Schiell and **Zena Thorpe**

We would also like to thank the following photographers:
Ray Daffurn of Visionbank, London, England, **Jack Mathieson, Geoffrey Carr, Elvin Derrick** and **Gary Bankhead**

Dates have been reproduced with permission, from data supplied by **HM Nautical Almanac Office** © Copyright Science and Engineering Research Council and the Canadian High Commission, London, England

Grateful thanks to:
The Douglas Brothers, Hazel Smythe and **Ray and Katherine Daffurn** of Visionbank, London, England

1994

JANUARY
```
S  M  T  W  T  F  S
               1
2  3  4  5  6  7  8
9  10 11 12 13 14 15
16 17 18 19 20 21 22
23 24 25 26 27 28 29
30 31
```

FEBRUARY
```
S  M  T  W  T  F  S
      1  2  3  4  5
6  7  8  9  10 11 12
13 14 15 16 17 18 19
20 21 22 23 24 25 26
27 28
```

MARCH
```
S  M  T  W  T  F  S
      1  2  3  4  5
6  7  8  9  10 11 12
13 14 15 16 17 18 19
20 21 22 23 24 25 26
27 28 29 30 31
```

APRIL
```
S  M  T  W  T  F  S
                  1  2
3  4  5  6  7  8  9
10 11 12 13 14 15 16
17 18 19 20 21 22 23
24 25 26 27 28 29 30
```

MAY
```
S  M  T  W  T  F  S
1  2  3  4  5  6  7
8  9  10 11 12 13 14
15 16 17 18 19 20 21
22 23 24 25 26 27 28
29 30 31
```

JUNE
```
S  M  T  W  T  F  S
         1  2  3  4
5  6  7  8  9  10 11
12 13 14 15 16 17 18
19 20 21 22 23 24 25
26 27 28 29 30
```

JULY
```
S  M  T  W  T  F  S
               1  2
3  4  5  6  7  8  9
10 11 12 13 14 15 16
17 18 19 20 21 22 23
24 25 26 27 28 29 30
31
```

AUGUST
```
S  M  T  W  T  F  S
   1  2  3  4  5  6
7  8  9  10 11 12 13
14 15 16 17 18 19 20
21 22 23 24 25 26 27
28 29 30 31
```

SEPTEMBER
```
S  M  T  W  T  F  S
            1  2  3
4  5  6  7  8  9  10
11 12 13 14 15 16 17
18 19 20 21 22 23 24
25 26 27 28 29 30
```

OCTOBER
```
S  M  T  W  T  F  S
                  1
2  3  4  5  6  7  8
9  10 11 12 13 14 15
16 17 18 19 20 21 22
23 24 25 26 27 28 29
30 31
```

NOVEMBER
```
S  M  T  W  T  F  S
      1  2  3  4  5
6  7  8  9  10 11 12
13 14 15 16 17 18 19
20 21 22 23 24 25 26
27 28 29 30
```

DECEMBER
```
S  M  T  W  T  F  S
            1  2  3
4  5  6  7  8  9  10
11 12 13 14 15 16 17
18 19 20 21 22 23 24
25 26 27 28 29 30 31
```

1995

JANUARY
```
S  M  T  W  T  F  S
1  2  3  4  5  6  7
8  9  10 11 12 13 14
15 16 17 18 19 20 21
22 23 24 25 26 27 28
29 30 31
```

FEBRUARY
```
S  M  T  W  T  F  S
         1  2  3  4
5  6  7  8  9  10 11
12 13 14 15 16 17 18
19 20 21 22 23 24 25
26 27 28
```

MARCH
```
S  M  T  W  T  F  S
         1  2  3  4
5  6  7  8  9  10 11
12 13 14 15 16 17 18
19 20 21 22 23 24 25
26 27 28 29 30 31
```

APRIL
```
S  M  T  W  T  F  S
                  1
2  3  4  5  6  7  8
9  10 11 12 13 14 15
16 17 18 19 20 21 22
23 24 25 26 27 28 29
30
```

MAY
```
S  M  T  W  T  F  S
   1  2  3  4  5  6
7  8  9  10 11 12 13
14 15 16 17 18 19 20
21 22 23 24 25 26 27
28 29 30 31
```

JUNE
```
S  M  T  W  T  F  S
            1  2  3
4  5  6  7  8  9  10
11 12 13 14 15 16 17
18 19 20 21 22 23 24
25 26 27 28 29 30
```

JULY
```
S  M  T  W  T  F  S
                  1
2  3  4  5  6  7  8
9  10 11 12 13 14 15
16 17 18 19 20 21 22
23 24 25 26 27 28 29
30 31
```

AUGUST
```
S  M  T  W  T  F  S
      1  2  3  4  5
6  7  8  9  10 11 12
13 14 15 16 17 18 19
20 21 22 23 24 25 26
27 28 29 30 31
```

SEPTEMBER
```
S  M  T  W  T  F  S
                  1  2
3  4  5  6  7  8  9
10 11 12 13 14 15 16
17 18 19 20 21 22 23
24 25 26 27 28 29 30
```

OCTOBER
```
S  M  T  W  T  F  S
1  2  3  4  5  6  7
8  9  10 11 12 13 14
15 16 17 18 19 20 21
22 23 24 25 26 27 28
29 30 31
```

NOVEMBER
```
S  M  T  W  T  F  S
         1  2  3  4
5  6  7  8  9  10 11
12 13 14 15 16 17 18
19 20 21 22 23 24 25
26 27 28 29 30
```

DECEMBER
```
S  M  T  W  T  F  S
               1  2
3  4  5  6  7  8  9
10 11 12 13 14 15 16
17 18 19 20 21 22 23
24 25 26 27 28 29 30
31
```